Ransom Neutron Stars
Platform 7
by Stephen Rickard

Published by Ransom Publishing Ltd.
Unit 7, Brocklands Farm, West Meon, Hampshire GU32 1JN, UK
www.ransom.co.uk

ISBN   978 178591 431 7
First published in 2017

Platform

Stephen Rickard

It is the end of a long year.

It was a wicked year, a dark year, when we had to fight to secure this planet for our children.

Now there are just a few of us left. We are less than one hundred, for sure.

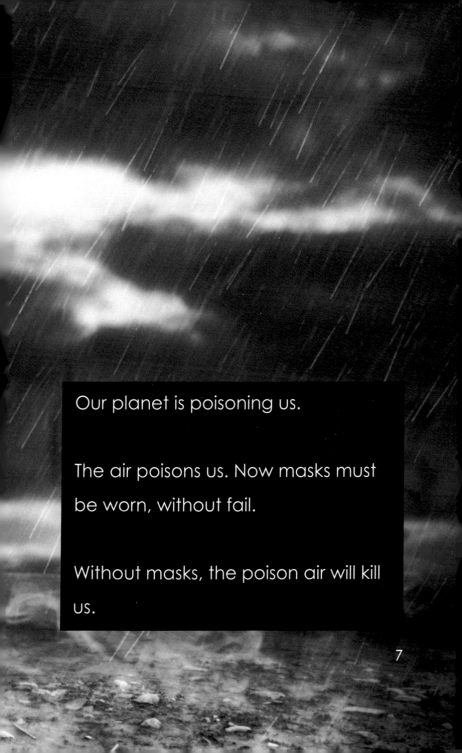

Our planet is poisoning us.

The air poisons us. Now masks must be worn, without fail.

Without masks, the poison air will kill us.

The soil poisons us.

We must cook all food, or it will kill us.

The rivers poison us too.

We cannot drink from the rivers.

For us, all of this planet is now toxic.

It is hard not to weep for this planet.

It is hard not to weep for us on this planet.

The Zeds did this to us.

They poisoned the planet.

The Zeds are killing us, just as this planet is now killing us.

Now some of us are hunting down the Zeds.

We are Platform 7.

Platform 7 hunts Zeds.

I am a member of Platform 7 and I will not rest until the Zeds are banished.

15

A kid visits the Platform 7 camp.

"I have seen the Zeds," he tells us.

"They are in the big shopping complex across town."

This is good to hear.

Now we can stop the Zeds. Now we can end all this for good.

We get in to our cars and trucks and rush to the shopping complex.

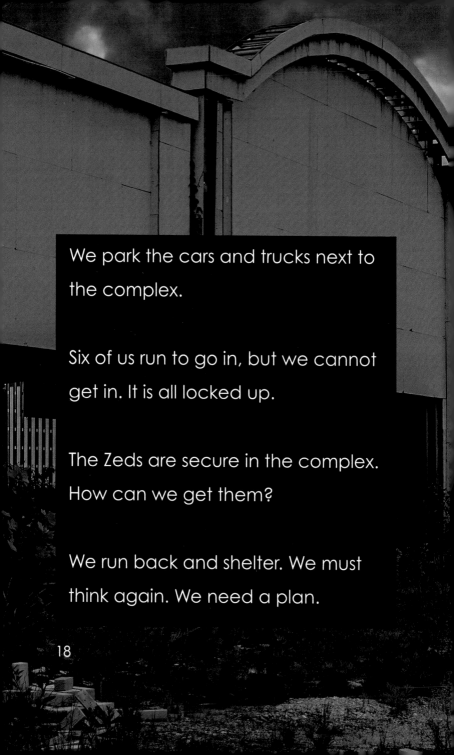

We park the cars and trucks next to the complex.

Six of us run to go in, but we cannot get in. It is all locked up.

The Zeds are secure in the complex. How can we get them?

We run back and shelter. We must think again. We need a plan.

19

We fill a truck with bricks.

Then we let the truck run in to the
shopping complex.

It hits the complex and there is a big
crack.

The truck jumps in the air and burns.

Now we can get in.

22

We start to run to the gap in the complex, when hundreds of Zeds run out of the complex. They are running to us and they are yelling at us.

We all feel a sudden fear.

We think they will attack us,

but they do not.

They grab us and march us in to the

shopping complex.

We march along long, dark
corridors. The lights are off –
there is no power.

What do they need from us?
What will they do to us?

They march us to the boss.
She has smears and cuts
on her.

I march up to the boss
and stand next to her.
She looks at me with
a sneer.

Her eyes are mad.
Her smell is bad.

"What is left of this planet is for us now," she growls.

"You cannot gulp this air. It poisons you. For us, this air is good. We do not need masks. You cannot drink from the rivers. The rivers poison you. For us, the rivers are good."

She looks at me. "This planet is no longer good for you. You are all history. We are the champions in this fight."

I think her long speech is over.
But she starts again.

"You are not important to us.
So we will let you go. Soon
the air and the rivers will
kill you. Then this planet
will be just for us."

"But do not attempt to attack us. We are strong, we are fit and there are lots of us. If you attack us, we will have to kill you.

"Now go. Go and spend the rest of the years out of my sight."

33

We turn and go. She stands
and looks at us go.

She is right. We cannot fight them.
We cannot win.

This planet is no longer for us.
We are all lost.

How much longer do we have
on this planet?